THIS JOURNAL BELONGS TO:

_____

_____

ORCHARD BOOKS
First published in the USA by Scholastic Inc in 2018
First published in Great Britain in 2019 by The Watts Publishing Group

1 3 5 7 9 10 8 6 4 2

A CIP catalogue record for this book is available from the British Library.

ISBN 978 1 40835 770 5

Printed and bound in China

MIX
Paper from
responsible sources
FSC
www.fsc.org
FSC® C104740

Orchard Books
An imprint of Hachette Children's Group
Part of The Watts Publishing Group Limited
Carmelite House
50 Victoria Embankment
London EC4Y 0DZ

An Hachette UK Company
www.hachette.co.uk
www.hachettechildrens.co.uk

TRAINER'S JOURNAL

ALL ABOUT ME

Rowlet, Litten and Popplio are Alola's first partner Pokémon!

Fill in your information below to start your Trainer's Journal!

Name:

Age:

Pokémon companion:

Regions travelled:

I am as brave as:

I am as fast as:

I am as tough as:

I am as fierce as:

When I'm not playing Pokémon, I like to:

I'd rather join Team Rocket than:

MY FAVOURITE POKÉMON

Write your favourite Pokémon below.
What region are they from?

KOMALA

ROCKRUFF

Why not draw some of the Pokémon, too!

COOL POKÉMON MOVES

Pikachu is an Electric-type Pokémon. Two of its powerful moves are Thunderbolt and Thunder.

WRITE YOUR FAVOURITE POKÉMON MOVES BELOW!

Pokémon:

Coolest Move:

Pokémon:

Coolest Move:

Pokémon:

Coolest Move:

Pokémon:

Coolest Move:

WHO'S IN MY POKÉ BALL?

What are the best Pokémon you've ever caught?
How did you catch them?

Pokémon:

I caught this Pokémon:

Pokémon:

I caught this Pokémon:

Pokémon:

I caught this Pokémon:

Ash's first catch in
Alola was Rowlet!

MY OWN PERSONAL POKÉ BALL >>>>>

What would your dream Poké Ball look like?
Draw it below and then write about what it can do.

My Poké Ball can:

ULTRA BALL

MASTER
BALL

GREAT BALL

Copy the picture of Rotom Dex into the grid below square by square. Then colour it in!

Rotom Dex was given to Ash by Professor Kukui. It is an electronic Pokédex and knows everything about Pokémon!

What Pokémon have you caught recently?
List them below.

A DAY IN THE LIFE OF ASH AND PIKACHU

8 a.m.	Wake up and eat delicious breakfast. Feed my and Professor Oak's Pokémon.
9 a.m.	Walk to the Pokémon School to learn lots about the Pokémon of Alola!
12 p.m.	Meet a new Pokémon at lunch! Challenge it to a friendly battle.
2 p.m.	Head out after school with my new friends, Kiawe, Mallow, Lana and Sophocles.
5 p.m.	Go back to Professor Oak's house and study Pokémon with Rotom Dex.

MY LIFE AS A TRAINER

Now write about a day in your life as a
Pokémon Trainer! Where would you go? What
cool Pokémon would you meet?

8 a.m.

9 a.m.

12 p.m.

2 p.m.

5 p.m.

7 p.m.

DREAM TEAM

In Alola Ash always has Pikachu, Rowlet and Rotom Dex by his side. You never know when Team Rocket might show up! Can you show Ash the way to his Pokémon?

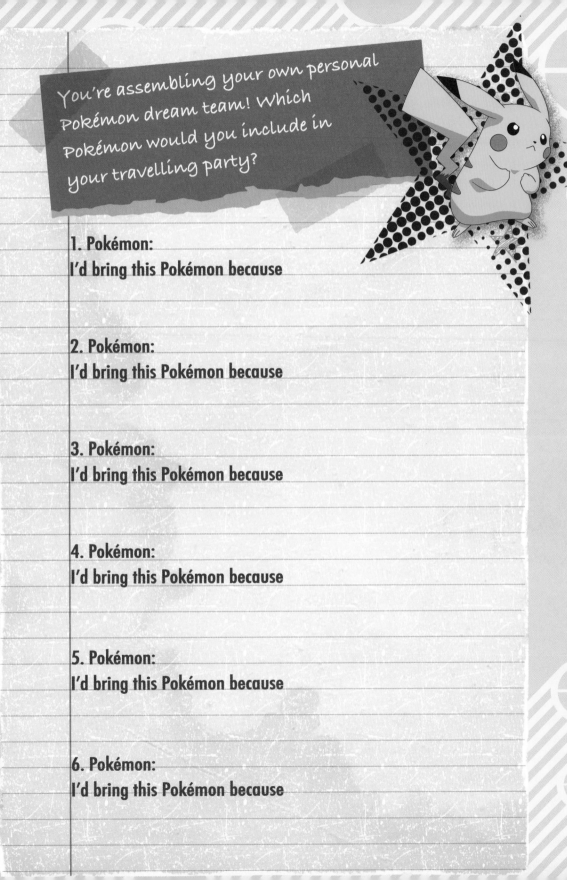

You're assembling your own personal Pokémon dream team! Which Pokémon would you include in your travelling party?

1. Pokémon:

I'd bring this Pokémon because

2. Pokémon:

I'd bring this Pokémon because

3. Pokémon:

I'd bring this Pokémon because

4. Pokémon:

I'd bring this Pokémon because

5. Pokémon:

I'd bring this Pokémon because

6. Pokémon:

I'd bring this Pokémon because

BIG BATTLES

Ash and Pikachu have been involved in some pretty epic Pokémon battles! Together with Pikachu, Ash knows he can overcome any enemy.

MY BIG BATTLES

What are some of the best Pokémon battles you've ever had? Write about them below!

⊙ _____ vs. _____

What happened?

⊙ _____ vs. _____

What happened?

⊙ _____ vs. _____

What happened?

⊙ _____ vs. _____

What happened?

⊙ _____ vs. _____

What happened?

MARVELLOUS MATCH-UPS

Pokémon battles can be a chance for Trainers to test out skills with their Pokémon. Can you name the battling Pokémon below?

	VS.	

	VS.	

	VS.	

Which Pokémon would you like to see in battle? Write about your dream match-ups in the spaces below. Who would win each contest?

.... **VS.** ....

The winner: ....

.... **VS.** ....

The winner: ....

.... **VS.** ....

The winner: ....

.... **VS.** ....

The winner: ....

MY FUNNIEST
MATCH-UPS

What are some of the goofiest Pokémon match-ups you can imagine? Write about them in the spaces below.

.... **VS.** ....

The winner: ....

.... **VS.** ....

The winner: ....

.... **VS.** ....

The winner: ....

.... **VS.** ....

The winner: ....

MY DREAM POKÉMON SCHOOL

When Ash is in Alola, he attends the Pokémon School where he learns all about the many different types of Pokémon in the region.

Ash makes lots of new friends at the school and even stays with one of the teachers, Professor Kukui, while he is there.

DID YOU KNOW?
The Pokévmon School has been open for over 20 years.

If you could go to Pokémon School like Ash and Pikachu what would it look like? Draw your ideal Pokémon academy below!

POKÉMON SCHOOL CLASSES

Ash may know a lot about the Pokémon in his home region of Kanto but when it comes to Alola Pokémon, it's a whole different ball game!

To make sure Ash is up to speed, the Pokémon School has lots of super cool classes taught by Professor Kukui.

COOL POKÉMON CLASSES

If you went to the Pokémon School, what classes would you want to take? Describe them below.

 Class:

🔘 **Class:**

🔘 **Class:**

TERRIFIC TRAINER TRAITS

Ash makes lots of new friends at the Pokémon School. Each has their own unique traits. Which Trainer do you have most in common with?

Ash Ketchum: A ten-year-old boy from Pallet Town in the Kanto region, Ash's goal is to become a Pokémon Master.

Kiawe: Kiawe is always calm, cool and collected. His Pokémon partner is a Charizard passed down from his grandfather.

Lana: Lana is a quiet girl and sometimes has a hard time expressing herself. But she is also very determined and has a strong will.

Lillie: Lillie is sweet and always kind. She knows a lot about Pokémon and is eager to learn more. When she talks about Pokémon, she sometimes sounds like a Pokédex.

Mallow: Mallow is energetic and spontaneous. She's a good cook (her family owns a local restaurant) and an even better athlete.

Sophocles: Sophocles is an excellent computer programmer with a habit of scratching his head and messing up his hair.

IF YOU WERE A TRAINER

Ash is determined to become a Pokémon Master one day. In order to achieve this, he trains hard and learns everything he can about Pokémon.

Although Ash has many Pokémon, Pikachu has been with him since the beginning.

Draw yourself as a Trainer like Ash. What type of Pokémon would you specialise in?

CREATE & DESIGN YOUR OWN POKÉMON

If you could create two brand-new Pokémon, what would they look like?

What are your Pokémon's stats?

My Pokémon's name: _____

Category: The _____**Pokémon**

Type: _____

Height: _____

Weight: _____

Moves: _____

_____

_____

Description: _____

_____

My Pokémon's name: _____

Category: The _____**Pokémon**

Type: _____

Height: _____

Weight: _____

Moves: _____

_____

_____

Description: _____

_____

GOTTA CATCH 'EM ALL!™

Different Pokémon require different tactics to capture them in battle. How would you capture these Pokémon?

1. Alolan Marowak: I'd capture this Pokémon by

2. Litten: I'd capture this Pokémon by

3. Alolan Raichu: I'd capture this Pokémon by

4. Alolan Ninetales: I'd capture this Pokémon by

5. Turtonator: I'd capture this Pokémon by

6. Grubbin: I'd capture this Pokémon by

ULTIMATE TRAINER TRAITS

Ash is determined to become a Pokémon Master one day. With Pikachu by his side he knows he can't fail, but Pikachu has got lost! Can you help Ash find his way to Pikachu?

What traits do you think are most important for a Pokémon Trainer? Circle the words below and then add your own!

Brave

Fast

Bad-tempered

Stealthy

Proud

Fierce

Strong

Lazy

Agile

Keen

Jealous

Kind

ALOLA PLATE RECIPE

Every Pokémon likes something a little different to eat! Mallow's family owns a restaurant in Alola so she is always thinking up exciting recipes!

Want to make a delicious dish for your Pokémon? What would you include in your recipe for an Alola plate?

INGREDIENTS:

INTRUCTIONS:

AWESOME ADVENTURES

What are some of your coolest Pokémon encounters? Write about them below!

COOL QUALITIES

What are some of your Pokémon's most amazing traits? Write the Pokémon's name below, and then list its cool qualities.

Pokémon:

Pokémon:

Pokémon:

Pokémon:

Pokémon:

⊙

Pokémon:

⊙

Pokémon:

⊙

TEAM ROCKET

Team Rocket wants to steal one of your most powerful Pokémon! How would you stop them?

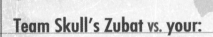

Now it's Team Skull's turn to challenge you! Which Pokémon would you use to stop them?

Team Skull's Zubat vs. your:

Describe the match:

Team Skull's Salandit vs. your:

Describe the match:

Team Skull's Gumshoos vs. your:

Describe the match:

CLASSIC VS. ALOLAN POKÉMON

How are these classic Pokémon different from
their Alolan forms? Which version would you
rather catch?

Exeggutor and Alolan Exeggutor

Muk and Alolan Muk

Raichu and Alolan Raichu

Meowth and Alolan Meowth

Ninetales and Alolan Ninetales

CREATE YOUR OWN ALOLAN POKÉMON

What classic Pokémon would you like to see in Alola with its own form? Draw what it would look like. Then describe how it looks different.

My Pokémon is: Alolan

Type:

Height:

Weight:

Moves:

Now write a Pokédex description for your

Alolan Pokémon:

INTIMIDATING POKÉMON

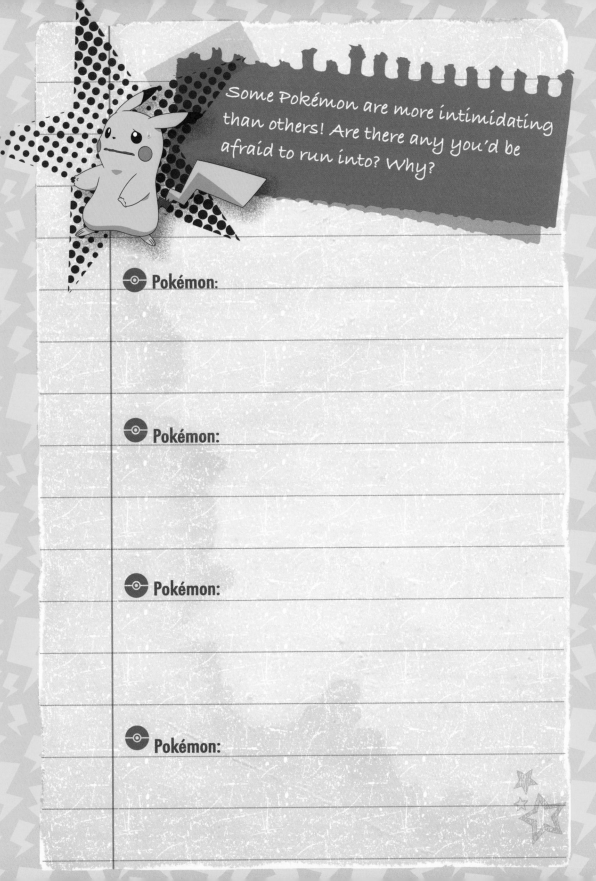

Some Pokémon are more intimidating than others! Are there any you'd be afraid to run into? Why?

🔴 **Pokémon:**

🔴 **Pokémon:**

🔴 **Pokémon:**

🔴 **Pokémon:**

HARD-TO-CATCH POKÉMON

Some Pokémon play hard to get! Which ones do you think are the hardest to capture? Why?

◉ Pokémon:

◉ Pokémon:

◉ Pokémon:

◉ Pokémon:

COOL AND QUIRKY POKÉMON

Certain Pokémon are known for being a bit peculiar. Which Pokémon do you find a little odd? Why?

🔴 **Pokémon:**

🔴 **Pokémon:**

🔴 **Pokémon:**

🔴 **Pokémon:**

MY POKÉMON PALS

If your friends were Pokémon, what type would they be? Share their stats in the spaces below.

Name:

Type:

Insert photo or draw your friend's picture here

Height: Weight:

Moves:

Insert photo or draw your friend's picture here

Name: **Type:**

Height: **Weight:**

Moves:

Insert photo or draw your friend's picture here

Name:

Type:

Height:

Weight:

Moves:

PACKING FOR YOUR POKÉMON JOURNEY

It's time to start your Pokémon quest! What would you bring with you on your journey? Here's what's in Ash's pack:

An extra cap

Poké Balls (of course!)

Pokédex

Sweatshirt

Snacks and berries for Pikachu

What would you take with you?

Z-RING

If you could make your own Z-Ring, what would it look like? Draw it here, and then label its special features.

THE ISLAND GUARDIAN

Tapu Koko is the Guardian of Melemele Island. What traits do you think make an amazing Island Guardian?

You and a friend are battling head-to-head. Describe how the battle plays out.

My: _____ vs. _____'s

Draw the battle in the space below.

Ash and Kiawe are having a friendly Pokémon battle! How would the match unfold?

ASH'S EPIC ADVENTURES

Ash has had some pretty amazing adventures during his time in Alola. What are some of your favourite moments?

SUPER SKILLS

What traits do you think make a great Pokémon?

- Good defence

ADVICE FROM A MASTER

Imagine you could ask Ash any question.
What would you ask?

 When did you first want to be become a Pokemon Master?

ASH VS. MALLOW

Ash and Mallow are having a friendly Pokémon battle. How would the match unfold?

QUEST CHALLENGES

What are some of the greatest hurdles
you've encountered on your Pokémon quest?
List them here.

YOUR ULTIMATE DESTINATION

You're traveling through Alola!
What's your first stop?

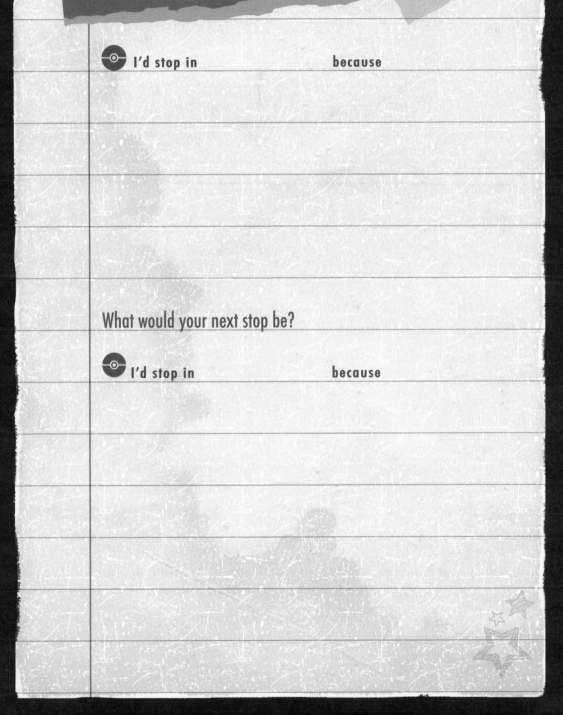

I'd stop in   because

What would your next stop be?

I'd stop in   because

TRAINING TIME!

What do you think you need to do to be the very best Trainer you can be?

- Practice
-
-
-
-
-

POKÉMON PRANKS

What are your favorite Pokémon jokes and sayings? Write them in the lines below.

⊙ Why did Popplio cross the road?

To get to the other tide!

⊙

⊙

⊙

⊙

⊙

You and a friend are battling head-to-head.
Describe how the battle plays out.

Your: _____ vs. _____'s

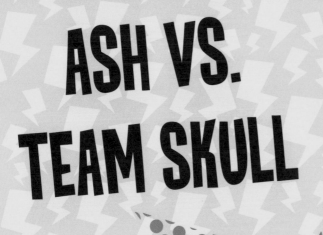

ASH VS.
TEAM SKULL

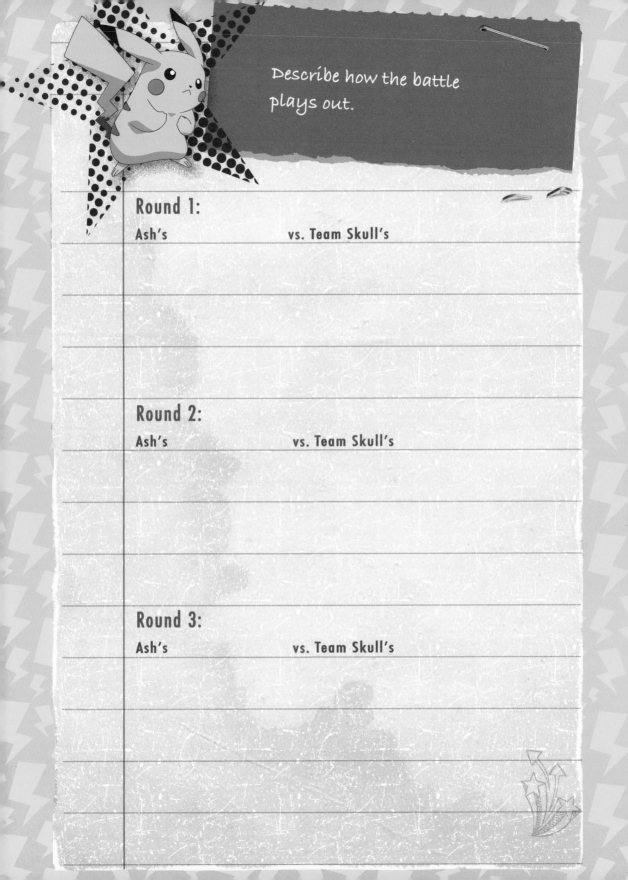

Describe how the battle plays out.

Round 1:
Ash's _____ vs. Team Skull's _____

Round 2:
Ash's _____ vs. Team Skull's _____

Round 3:
Ash's _____ vs. Team Skull's _____

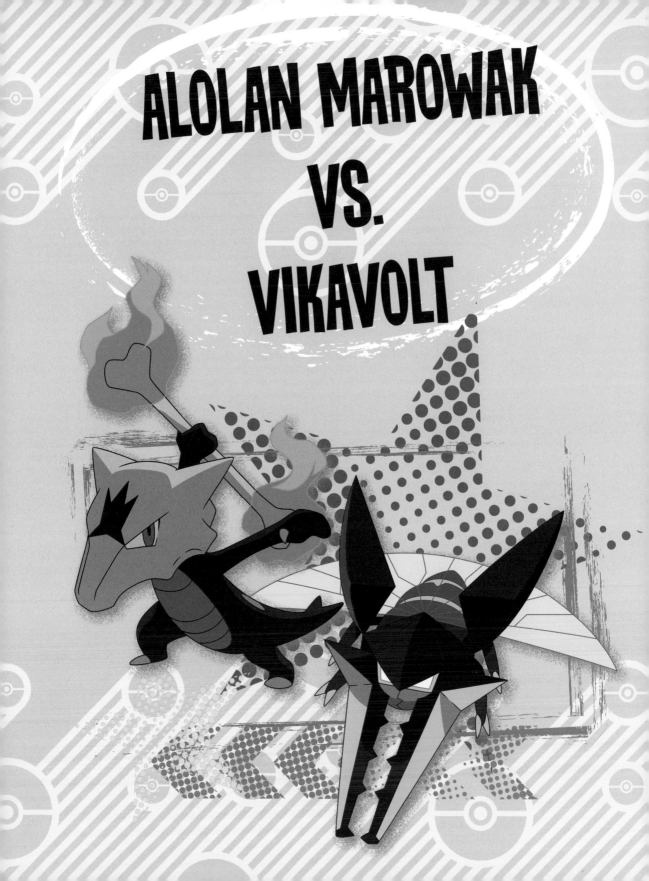

How would the battle unfold?

NEW ADVENTURES

What should happen on Ash's next adventure?
Describe it here.

ANSWERS

Pikachu	VS.	Mimikyu
Rowlet	VS.	Sandygast
Litten	VS.	Persian